1st grade Sight Words

who	able	why	fun	same	second	light	draw
when	bad	car	sky	knew	does	seen	state
them	give	book	both	begin	together	during	kind
because	today	good	time	winter	house	wrong	circle
just	week	help	sea	must	start	you're	large
little	something	city	wrote	stop	grew	several	doing
before	bus	write	again	happy	way	never	family
mother	year	top	carry	catch	deep	getting	clothes
where	can't	room	wait	third	view	earth	hand
very	tell	under	each	night	snow	group	different
could	across	fast	feel	goes	friends	baby	river
were	world	hill	always	last	story	everything	might
over	cat	know	first	school	street	high	air
ride	take	use	ask	walk	above	wouldn't	I'd
don't	dad	let	food	maybe	find	probably	suddenly
said	hide	place	work	change	between	through	easy
that	almost	sleep	brother	outside	every	against	finally
with	dog	love	though	part	should	hours	everyone
their	anything	much	funny	live	father	fight	hold
what	home	stay	gave	party	watch	once	special
but	down	name	thing	game	children	best	animal
here	become	new	close	try	enough	ready	lost
going	end	paper	even	pick	dark	free	beautiful
our	behind	rain	grow	right	great	show	need
want	fish	door	gone	until	inside	building	job

Made in the USA
Coppell, TX
04 July 2023

18750109R00046